# Shabbos Heroes

by Yussie and Esther Fingerer

illustrated by Shaindy Brull

שירה Shira Press

In Honor of
Rabbi and Mrs. Simcha Bunim Cohen Shlita,

May you continue to guide and inspire our Kehilla
and all Klal Yisroel Bederech Yisroel Sabbah.

# Table of Contents

ISBN 0-9758683-0-6

Published and distributed by
Shira Press
1403 Twin Oaks Drive
Lakewood, NJ 08701
(732) 901-9598

Graphic design and layout by
Chavie Friedman (732) 886-5346

Printed in China

# The Tablecloth

It was a Friday morning in Cracow, Poland in 1529. Reb Yisroel Isser was working in his fabric store. In walked a very important customer.

"I need lots of different materials today," said the customer. "I must bring material to the tailor. He will sew clothing for the king and queen."

"I close every Friday at twelve o'clock," said Reb Yisroel Isser. "I can help you until then."

He showed the customer many different rolls of material. It was taking a long time for the customer to make up his mind.

Reb Yisroel Isser looked at the clock. "I have to close in fifteen minutes," he said.

But the customer was taking his time.

"It is twelve o'clock now," said Reb Yisroel Isser. "I have to close my store now."

"But I am not ready yet," answered the customer.

"I am sorry," said Reb Yisroel Isser. "I always close my store early on Friday in honor of Shabbos."

"I will buy so much from you," said the customer. "You will make lots of money. If you close now I will never come to your store again."

5

"I know I will lose lots of money," answered Reb Yisroel Isser. "But Shabbos is more precious than all the money in the world."

He led the customer out of the store and locked the door.

Hashem saw how much Reb Yisroel Isser loved Shabbos. Hashem gave him a reward much greater than money. Hashem gave him a special son. He and his wife named the baby Moshe.

When Moshe grew up he became a great Talmid Chochom. He was known as the Rema which stands for Rabbi Moshe Isserlish (son of Isser).

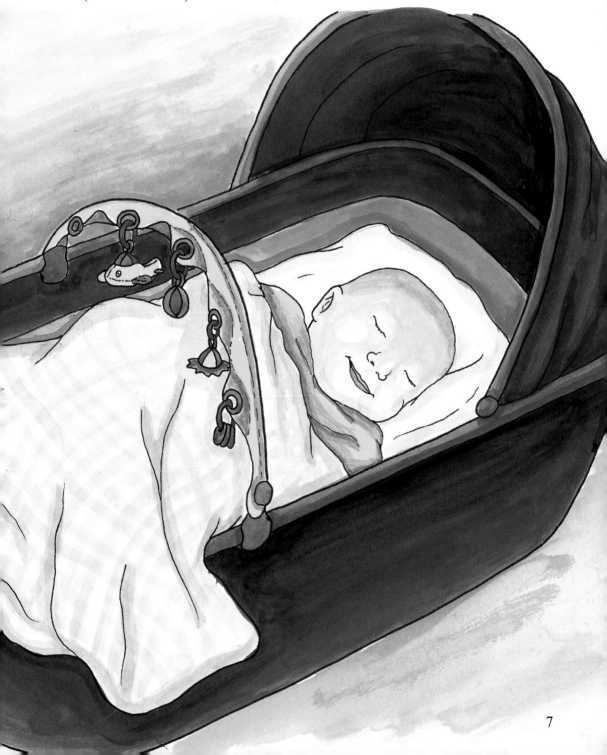

The Rema's halachic decisions on the Shulchan Aruch are called the "Mapa," which means tablecloth. It was a special reward for his father who refused to sell cloth on Friday afternoon. He honored the Shabbos and was rewarded greatly.

Sources: <u>Tales of Tzaddikim</u>, Mesorah Publications 1987
        G. Matov, Volume 2 pg. 238
        "Olomeinu," December 2001

# The Special Baggage

Rabbi and Mrs. Yaakov Yosef Herman were moving to Eretz Yisroel. They packed up all their clothes, books, dishes and belongings, and put them into boxes and suitcases. Then they went with their baggage on a big ship to Eretz Yisroel.

It was a very long trip. The trip usually took two weeks. Instead it took even longer. The ship docked at the port on Friday an hour before sunset.

"We do not have time to get all our baggage," said Rabbi Herman to his wife. "I will just take my special suitcase with my Sefer Torah and Tallis and Tefillin."

"I will just take my pocketbook," said Mrs. Herman.

They went to the customs officer.

"Please stamp our passports and let us go. We will come

back after Shabbos and pick up our baggage," said Rabbi Herman.

"If you leave your baggage here, no one will watch it," said the officer. "Robbers will take it and you will be left with nothing!"

"We have no choice. We must be on time for Shabbos," answered Rabbi Herman.

"Wow!" exclaimed the officer. " You are willing to lose all your possessions for Shabbos. That is amazing!"

He stamped their passports and let them go.

Rabbi and Mrs. Herman took a taxi. They came to their friend Rabbi Alfa's house just in time for candle lighting.

It was a beautiful Shabbos. The Hermans kept thinking of the special mitzvah they did by giving up all their belongings for Shabbos.

After Shabbos Rabbi Alfa said to them, "Let's go together to the port. Maybe some of your boxes are still there."

So Rabbi Alfa and Rabbi and Mrs. Herman went together to the port.

At the port, they saw a little light at the end of the pier.

"Who is that?" called a voice out to them.

"We are some passengers who came off a ship yesterday," answered Rabbi Herman.

The guard came close to them. "What is your name?" he asked.

"Yaakov Herman," answered Rabbi Herman.

"Oh! I was waiting for you!" said the guard. "I was watching your baggage for you. Here it is."

The customs officer had hired the guard after seeing the Hermans' dedication to Shabbos.

The Hermans took their baggage to their new home in Yerushalayim.

Source: All For the Boss, Feldheim Publishers 2001
Ruchoma Shain, page 335

# I Will Never Write on Shabbos!

A young man named Yosef came to Canada during the Second World War. The Canadian government thought that Yosef was helping their enemies and telling them their secrets. They called him a spy and put him in jail.

Many people knew that Yosef was not a spy. They tried to help him. They spoke to lots of important government people. A year later the people in the government agreed to let Yosef out of jail.

A special guard was sent on Friday to let Yosef out of jail. The guard came after Shabbos had already begun.

He said to Yosef, "I am here to take you home. Just sign

your name on this line and you will be free."

"I can't," said Yosef. "It is Shabbos."

"YOU WHAT?" yelled the guard. "You better sign this paper now or you will just have to stay here!"

"I will never write on Shabbos!" said Yosef. "I do not care if you make me stay in jail. I will not write on Shabbos!"

The guard left Yosef in jail.

Many important people spoke to the government again. Two weeks later the government let Yosef out of jail.

Yosef went to yeshiva. He became a great Talmid Chochom.

Source: Reb Yaakov, Mesorah Publications 1993
Yonason Rosenblum, page 145

# Where is Zaida?

**I**t was a winter Friday morning in 1973. Zaida was traveling to Toronto from Syracuse on the New York State Thruway. As he entered Buffalo it started to snow.

"There is so much snow," thought Zaida. "It is good that I left early in the morning so I will be home in time for Shabbos."

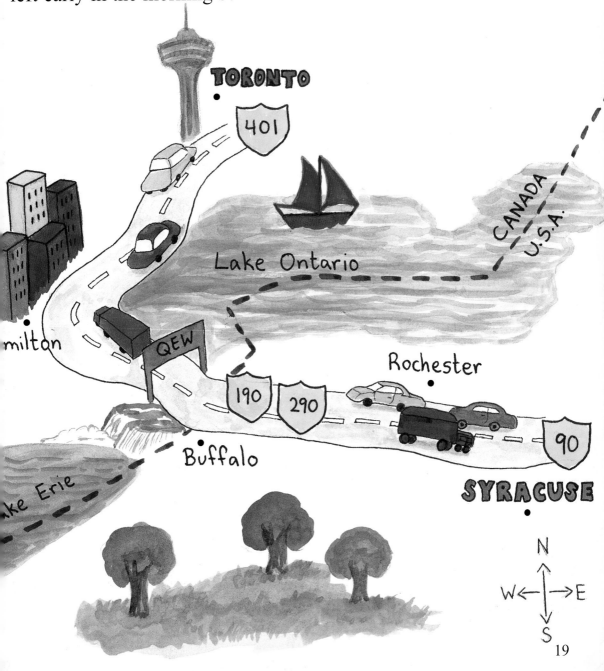

Zaida crossed the border into Canada. As he drove through Hamilton the snow became much heavier. Three big snowplows were clearing the roads. All the cars behind them were moving very slowly.

"Will I get home in time for Shabbos?" worried Zaida.

In those days people did not have cell phones. Zaida could not call Bubby to tell her where he was.

It was getting closer and closer to Shabbos. Zaida looked at the signs on the highway. He was already in Toronto, but he was very far from home.

Zaida exited the highway and parked his car at a gas station. He took his wallet out of his pocket, left it in the car and locked the door.

"Here are my car keys," said Zaida to the gas station attendant. "It is forbidden for me to drive anymore. I will walk home and pick up my car tomorrow night."

At home, Bubby had already lit the candles. All the children were very worried. Zaida had not come home.

Bubby and the children made Kiddush and then Hamotzi. The children looked out the window. Maybe they would see Zaida. They could see the snow falling and hear the wind howling. But Zaida was not there.

"Come and finish the meal," said Bubby.

Everyone ate the meal. It was very lonely. They bentched and went upstairs to bed.

Suddenly, there was a knock on the door. Everyone jumped out of bed and ran downstairs. Bubby looked through the peephole and saw that it was… ZAIDA! Bubby opened the door and Zaida came inside.

Zaida's face was all red and he was covered with snow. He had walked for two and a half hours and he was finally home. Everyone was very happy. Zaida, Bubby and the children had a warm and peaceful Shabbos.

Source: Rabbi Moshe Alon

The
Wheat
Kernel

by YUSSIE and ESTHER FINGERER
illustrated by SHEPSIL SCHEINBERG

Watch the little wheat kernel as it sprouts and grows into a beautiful wheat stalk, hoping for the day when its flour will be used for a mitzvah. Will the wheat's tefillos be answered, or will the baker use it for something else first? Join the wheat kernel on this exciting and colorful adventure.